HISTORY QUICK READ NO. 3
1642-1789

TAKING SIDES (1642)
FLAMES AT THE DOOR (1666)
A ROYAL SPLASH (1789)

by David Oakden

Illustrated by Stephen Millingen and Edward Blake

First published in 1993
by Anglia Young Books
Durhams Farmhouse
Ickleton
Saffron Walden, Essex CB10 1SR

Illustrations by Stephen Millingen and Edward Blake

British Library Cataloguing-in-Publication Data
A catalogue record for this book is available from the
British Library

ISBN 1 871173 25 6

Typeset in Sassoon Primary and printed in Great Britain
by Redwood Books, Trowbridge, Wilts.

CONTENTS

TAKING SIDES, 1642

The dog found the body. The King's messenger lay in a ditch with his throat cut. Sir Edmund Verney called his dog. The dog would not come. Sir Edmund came closer. He saw that the dead man was clutching part of a letter.

The letter was torn and smears of blood had made the ink run. But the message was clear. It said, 'The King's army is gathering at Edgehill. Bring the Royal Standard and get ready for battle.' It was signed by King Charles.

Sir Edmund called for his servants. 'Get my horse!' he shouted. 'I must ride today. The King is at war with Parliament.'

At the same time, Sir Edmund's nephew, John Verney, was studying at Oxford. He was thirteen years old and a clever boy. But he was not keen on work. He liked playing football.

He liked hunting rabbits.

One day he was walking across the college lawn. Suddenly someone pulled his hair. He turned round angrily. An old man in a black robe was scowling at him. It was Dr Kettell, his tutor.

Dr Kettell tugged John's long hair again. 'Get it cut!' he growled. 'And take off that bright tunic. Students must wear black.'

John bowed and walked away. But he felt very angry. He did not want to study all the time. He liked having long hair.

When John got back to his room, he found two letters. One was from Sir Edmund. 'Come and join the King's army,' it said. 'Leave your studies and fight for God and the King against Parliament.'

The other letter was from his cousin, Ralph. 'I shall be near Oxford tomorrow,' it said. 'Come and join Parliament's army. Leave your studies and fight for God and Parliament against the King.'

'Is God on both sides then?' said John to himself.

That night he went to his evening meal. Dr Kettell was there.

'What work have you done today?' asked the tutor.

'None, sir,' said John. 'I went hunting rabbits.'

Dr Kettell was angry. 'You lazy good-for-nothing!' he said. 'And I told you to get your hair cut!'

He grabbed a kitchen knife and held John round the neck.

He sawed at John's hair. Soon the floor was littered with long curls.

'Good,' said the tutor. 'Now you look better.'

John ran out of the dining room. That settled it. He would go and fight. Then he stopped. Which side should he join? Should he fight for the King? Or should he fight for Parliament?

That night he crept out of a side gate. A coach was in the shadows. Two men stood by it.

Then another man came from the college. He was carrying a heavy sack. He put the sack down and turned to go back.

'One more load to fetch,' he said. John shrank into the shadows. It was Dr Kettell. What was he up to?

As the men threw the sack into the coach it fell open. A metal plate rolled along the road and stopped at John's feet.

John picked it up. It was solid gold!

'Stop thieves!' he yelled.

Before he could say any more, John was knocked to the ground.

One of the men knelt on his chest and held a knife to his throat.

'A Parliament man,' he said grimly. 'Look at his short hair. Let's kill him.'

John was terrified.

But the other man said, 'No. No killing here. Stop his noise and let's get away. The rest of the stuff can wait.'

A cloth was tied over John's head and he was bundled into the coach.

'Get in there and shut up!' hissed a voice. 'Remember I'm sitting by you. Just make one move and you're a dead man.'

The door slammed and they were off. After a while, the coach stopped. The door opened and John was dragged out. He blinked as the cloth was pulled off his head.

'Right. This place is as good as any,' said the man with the knife. 'Let's do it here.'

'Do what?' said John. 'Who are you? Why has Dr Kettell given you the college gold?'

'Too many questions,' said the man.

'But since you'll soon be dead, I'll tell you. We're off to join the King's army at Edgehill. As for the college gold, the King will sell it to pay the troops.'

'That's enough,' snarled the other man. 'Take the little spy into that wood over there and finish him off.'

'Just a minute,' said the man with the knife. 'There's a stone in my shoe.'

He took his shoe off to look for it.

John's legs felt weak and he was sweating with fear. He had to escape. But how?

Then he had an idea. On the ground was the cloth from his head. He picked it up and pretended to wipe his face with it.

Then he wandered round to the horse's head. Nobody was looking. With a yell, John flapped the cloth in the horse's face and then threw it over its eyes.

The horse was startled. It whinnied and reared up. The coach tipped over onto its side. The men yelled and jumped out of the way. John ran. He ran for a long time. Then he flopped down on the grass.

Suddenly he heard men's voices. He hid behind a tree. Now what? Had he escaped from one danger only to run into another?

Trembling, he waited till the men were close by. Then he peered out.

He couldn't believe it! One of them was his cousin Ralph.

'Ralph!' he shouted, and ran to him.

'John?' said Ralph. 'How did you get here? Have you come to join the Parliament army?'

John babbled out his tale. 'The College gold

and silver,' he said. 'It's in a coach. They are giving it to the King. They were going to kill me.'

A sturdy man with excited eyes said, 'Gold and silver? We must have it before it gets to the King.'

Ralph said, 'John, do you know who this is? This is Oliver Cromwell.'

John gasped. He had heard of this man. He was a great soldier and a Member of Parliament. John bowed low and said, 'I am glad to see you, sir.'

Cromwell smiled grimly. 'Then come and fight with me. We need young men like you. The war may be long. Many will die. But, in the end, Parliament will win and we shall be rid of this wicked King.'

He handed John a sword. 'Here,' he said. 'Take this and use it. Now, let's find those murderers.'

Cromwell and the others jumped on their horses. John got up behind Ralph and they galloped off.

Before long they heard the rumble of the coach. 'At them!' roared Cromwell and charged.

The fight was soon over. The man with the knife was killed and the other man was captured. Cromwell and his men took the coach on to Edgehill.

When they got there, Cromwell said, 'Well done, lad. You have served Parliament well.'

John looked around him. Everywhere men in armour were getting ready for battle. He said, 'What shall I do? My uncle is the King's standard bearer. How can I fight against my own family?'

'It is worse for me,' said Ralph. 'Your Uncle Edmund is my father, but I have to fight for what is right.'

'This is terrible,' said John. 'Families should not fight against each other.'

Ralph sighed. 'Listen,' he said. 'King Charles is a bad king. He raises huge taxes and then wastes the money on wars against the Scots which all go wrong. He will not listen to Parliament.'

'He does nothing for the common people. And now he is talking about changing the country back to being Roman Catholic. He is mad.'

'But Sir Edmund is your father ...' began John.

'My father told me that he did not like the quarrel. But he is the royal standard bearer, so he has no choice.'

A trumpet sounded and drums began to beat. Ralph put on a steel helmet and shook John's hand. 'I fight not for the family, but for God and Parliament,' he said and rode off to battle.

The battle raged all day at Edgehill. But John did not fight. He stayed with the silver and gold. He helped the wounded.

After it was all over he walked across the field.

There were bodies everywhere. Then, in the mud, he saw a face he knew. It was Sir Edmund, his uncle. He was dead.

John knelt down. There was a ring on one hand. It had a picture of the King on it. John slipped it off the cold finger.

'Goodbye, my brave uncle,' he said. 'I will take this ring to my aunt. But I am glad I did not fight. God was on neither side here.'

THE ENGLISH CIVIL WAR, 1642-8

King Charles was disliked by a lot of people. He loved having a good time. He wasted too much money. When he told Parliament to raise taxes, they refused.

He spent more money on fighting the Scots, then lost the battles. He talked of turning England back into a Roman Catholic country.

Parliament was horrified. They raised an army to force the King to change his ways. But the King also raised an army. So, from 1642 to 1648, there was a civil war.

Englishmen fought Englishmen. Families fought against each other. Many people lost their lives. The king's standard bearer, Sir Edmund Verney, died at Edgehill.

The King and his friends were called Cavaliers. Many of them had long, curly hair and wore fancy clothes.

The men on the other side often wore dark, simple clothes and had short hair. They were called Roundheads. Their most famous leader was Oliver Cromwell.

In the end Parliament won. King Charles had his head cut off. The country had no king for many years and Cromwell ruled as Lord Protector.

FLAMES AT THE DOOR, 1666

Martha Jackson was crying. 'It's no use,' she said. 'The baby is ill. We must do something to help him.'

The little boy's face was red and covered with spots. He was sweating and moving about. His eyes were puffy with crying. 'Is it the plague?' said her husband, Paul.

Martha looked round fearfully. 'Hush!' she said. 'Don't say that word.'

The two older girls, Jane and Rebecca, waited

downstairs. The look on their mother's face told them all they needed to know. Jane said, 'It's the plague, isn't it?'

Rebecca said, 'I don't want to die.' She burst into tears.

At that moment there was a loud knock at the door. Martha's hand flew to her mouth. 'Don't answer it. It's the plague-seekers,' she said. There was another knock, then a scratching sound, and then silence.

Paul went to the door and flung it open. There, painted on the wood, was a huge red cross.

That night the plague cart rumbled through the dark streets. A voice wailed, 'Bring out your dead. Bring out your dead.'

The family huddled together in the upstairs room. Martha wrote on a paper, 'Lord, Have Mercy on Us.' She nailed the paper on the door by the red cross.

'How long before we die?' whispered Rebecca.

Paul said, 'Hush. Have hope. How is the baby?'

Martha said, 'I bathed his face in cool water. But the spots are still there. How did the plague-seekers know?'

'Bad news travels fast,' said Paul.

They slept badly and the baby cried all night.

'No change,' said Martha next day. 'He's very ill. But Jane and Rebecca must go for food. Carry a white stick each. Then people will know that there is plague in our house. Take my purse and go to the market.'

Paul said, 'What about me?'

He worked in Pudding Lane with the King's baker.

'The baker would not want you to handle bread,' said Martha. 'And if it is the plague, nobody can go out, except to buy food, for a month.'

'Then I shall lose my job,' said Paul.

The girls came back with bread and meat. They were out of breath.

'It was terrible,' said Rebecca. 'Some boys threw mud at us. And nobody at the market wanted to serve us.'

'We had to put our money in a pail of water,' said Jane. 'They would not let us near the stall.'

'But the good news is that the plague is passing,' said Rebecca. 'We met Mistress Potts from next door. She said that ours is the first new case for six days.'

'She has sent some vinegar for you,' said Jane. 'She says it helps if you dab the spots with it.'

That night it rained. Martha opened the window. 'Thanks be to God,' she said. 'The rain will wash the streets.'

Paul said, 'I wish it could wash away the plague.'

The baby made a noise. 'Poor little thing,' said Martha. 'I must bathe his spots again.'

She crossed to the wooden cradle. Then she gave a shout. 'Paul! Look!'

'What is it?' asked Paul.

The baby was lying on his back. He was waving his legs in the air and chuckling. The spots had faded. It had not been the plague after all!

Next morning Paul scrubbed the red cross off the door. Then he went out. But another man had got his job at the King's baker.

He tried for work all over London. But nobody wanted him. The only job was at the bear pit.

'I cannot do that,' said Paul to Martha. 'I would rather starve. The man whips a blinded bear while dogs bite its legs.'

Jane said, 'How cruel! I wish somebody would let the bear go free.'

'Never mind the bear,' said Martha. 'How are we going to live? We only have a few pence left. We can't pay the rent or buy food if we have no money.'

Paul said, 'I must get a job before the winter. I know, I will go across the river and down into Kent. Perhaps there will be work out in the country.'

Next day he set off.

'I will be back in a few days,' he said. 'You must sell some of the furniture to get money for food.'

Two weeks later he was still not back. Martha had sold some furniture and bed-linen.

That night, she and the girls sat round the table. It was getting cold but they had no fire.

Jane said, 'What will happen to that bear?' Will he get food this winter?'

Martha said, 'Forget the bear, you silly girl. Think about us. Will we get food this winter?'

That night Martha was so worried that she did not go to bed. She dozed in a chair.

Then, very early in the morning, there was a noise at the door. It was Paul.

He said, 'Great news. I have found a job in a little town in Kent. There is a cottage with the job.'

Martha could hardly speak for joy.

'I'll get the girls up and we'll pack our things,' she said.

But the girls' bed was empty. They had gone!

Paul said, 'Stay with the baby. I'll go and look in the street.'

London was just waking up. Carts rumbled down the street. A flock of sheep was on its way to Smithfield Market. People were brushing rubbish out of their houses.

Nobody had seen the girls. Then Martha called, 'I've thought of something. Jane has been talking about the bear-pit. Go and look there.'

Paul ran. As he ran he smelt smoke in the air. Then in Pudding Lane he could see that there was a big fire at the baker's.

Men were pulling down burning thatch from the roof with hooks. The woodwork was crackling with flames. A strong wind was blowing sparks everywhere.

As Paul ran past, two more houses caught fire. 'I hope our house will be all right,' he thought.

In the next street it was even worse. Every house was on fire. People were trying to save furniture.

Paul struggled through the crowd. Where were Rebecca and Jane? Then he saw them. Rebecca was lying in the road. Jane was kneeling by her. Burning straw and wood were falling all round them.

For a moment he thought Rebecca was dead. Then she sat up and started coughing. Quickly Paul picked her up and ran, away from the flames.

'She fell,' panted Jane as they ran. 'Then the smoke got so thick that she fainted. I thought we should be burned to death.'

'Look!' shouted Paul. 'Our house! It's on fire! Martha! Where are you?'

Paul told the girls to stay in the street. He rushed into the house. Inside there were flames and smoke everywhere, but Martha had got the baby. She was putting a few things into a bundle.

'Get out!' said Paul. 'The house will collapse any minute. Take the baby and run.'

Outside Rebecca was feeling better. They all joined hands and ran for the river. Hundreds of people were standing on the bank, trying to find boats to get across to the other side.

'This is no use,' said Paul. 'Let's make for London Bridge.'

They got across the bridge just in time. The houses and shops on the bridge were all on fire. Pieces of blazing timber were falling with a hiss into the river.

At last they were safe on the south bank of the river. Behind them they heard a sudden explosion. Then there was another. And another.

'They are blowing up houses with gunpowder,' said Paul. 'They want to make gaps that the fire can't jump across.'

'We shall never see our house again,' said Martha. 'London's burning. It will never be the same. Look! Even St Paul's Cathedral is on fire.'

'Forget London,' said Paul. 'It looks bad, but good may come of it. The fire will clean away

the last of the plague. The city will be rebuilt.
There will be a new St Paul's. As for us, we are
off to a new home and a new job.'

And they turned away from London and began
to walk.

THE FIRE OF LONDON, 1666

The Great Plague of 1665 killed thousands. It was spread by fleas carried by rats.

In 1666 London had dirty, narrow streets. The wooden houses leaned over those streets, almost touching each other. Many of them had roofs thatched with straw. If a fire started it was very difficult to put out.

The great fire started at the King's baker's shop in Pudding Lane. It spread very quickly and soon most of London was on fire.

The old London Bridge burned. St Paul's Cathedral was destroyed.

The river was full of boats carrying people and furniture to safety.

To stop the fire spreading, houses were blown up. When the fire ended, London was rebuilt. A great man at the time was Christopher Wren. He designed the new St Paul's Cathedral.

The good result of the fire was the end of the plague.

A ROYAL SPLASH, 1789

The sea at Weymouth was rough. Huge waves roared up the beach and across the sand. The air was full of salty spray.

Betty Hand stood at the top of the beach and waved to her father, Charlie Hand.

His old horse was dragging a cart up the beach. The cart was painted white and had four large wheels.

At the back of it, six wooden steps led down from a door.

It was a bathing machine or bathing cart, a hut on wheels. People who wanted to bathe in the sea got undresed in it. A horse dragged the cart down the beach and into the sea. Then the horse was led away and the bather walked down the front steps into the waves.

Betty ran down the sands. 'Dad, have you heard the news?' she said.

Charlie Hand took off a boot and tipped sand and stones out of it. 'News?' he said. 'What news?'

'King George has been told by his doctors that a dip in the sea would do him good. He's coming here, to Weymouth!'

Charlie said, 'That could be good. If His Majesty wants to bathe, then he'll need a bathing cart. And who's got the best cart in Weymouth?'

'The Hand family!' said Betty.

'Don't talk rubbish,' said another voice. A dark man with greasy hair was listening. His name was Jack Spotkins.

'Your old cart's no use,' he said. 'A King needs one that is safe and dry and clean, like mine.'

Charlie said, 'We shall have to wait and see. But I'm going to give ours a new coat of paint, just in case.'

Betty said, 'And I'll groom the horse. I'm sure King George will choose our cart.' She felt very excited.

After two days, the bathing cart looked lovely. It was painted red and white and the little steps had been scrubbed and sanded.

Inside, Mrs Hand fitted a padded seat and Charlie nailed up a row of clothes hooks.

'You're wasting your time,' said Spotkins with a scowl. Charlie and Betty took no notice of him.

That night Betty slept badly. Early in the morning she went to the window and looked out over the beach.

The sun was rising. She could just see their bathing cart.

But something was wrong with it! It was
leaning over. The wooden roof had a hole in it.
A man was prowling round it. As she watched,
the man lifted a hammer and smashed a hole
in the door.

Betty screamed, 'Dad! Somebody's breaking up
the cart!'

They ran to the beach. The man had gone, but
the cart was wrecked.

The new paint was scratched. Two of the
wheels were off and one was broken. The steps
were lying in the sea. The coat hooks had gone
and the padded seat was ripped. It was a
disaster.

'Jack Spotkins did this, I'm sure,' said Betty.
'He wants the King to use his cart.'

'We can't prove it,' said Mr Hand. 'All we can
do is get to work to put it right. The King
comes tomorrow!'

As they worked a fat man came down the
beach. He wore fine clothes. His little legs
were in silk stockings and he had shiny shoes
with great buckles on them.

He was carrying a cane with a silver knob on the end. A servant in a powdered wig walked behind him.

The fat man took off his hat and mopped sweat from his face. Then he looked at Charlie's broken cart.

'Pooh! That's not fit for a dog,' he said.

As they watched, the man went to Jack Spotkins' cart. He looked in at the door and wrinkled his nose. 'Pooh!' he said again. 'It stinks of fish.'

Jack Spotkins rubbed his hands and bowed low. 'I'll scrub it out, my lord,' he said.

Charlie whispered to the servant, 'Who's your master?'

The servant sniffed. 'Lord Jameson,' he said. 'He's preparing the way for His Majesty the King.'

Another man in rich clothes came up. Two ladies wth sunshades stood on the road watching them.

'What beautiful clothes,' sighed Betty, looking down at her own faded smock and bare legs.

Lord Jameson shouted to the servant, 'Grimes! Take the ladies back to the boarding-house. Sir Percy and I will try the water. This fellow's cart looks as good as any.'

He went inside and the other man followed him. The door shut and Spotkins' horse pulled the cart down into the waves.

Spotkins took the horse away and he stood back, bowing and rubbing his hands.

Betty stood on the sand, watching.

A wind had got up and there were spots of rain in the air. Out at sea a fishing boat was tossing up and down.

'They'd better be careful,' thought Betty. 'There's a storm coming.'

The door at the front of the bathing machine opened and out came Lord Jameson. He walked down the steps and a wave splashed his legs.

'I say, it's very cold,' he said. 'But come along, Percy. Don't stand on the steps dithering.'

Sir Percy said, 'I've sent that fellow Spotkins for some brandy. We shall need a drink after this.'

Betty saw Jack Spotkins just going out of sight. Her father had gone as well to fetch some tools. She was alone on the beach.

'Come along, Percy,' shouted Lord Jameson. He was now up to his waist in the sea.

Percy went down a step. 'Am I safe?' he said anxiously. 'I can't swim.'

The sky had gone black. The storm was very close.

A flash of lightening lit up the sky. Huge waves crashed onto the beach. Rain hissed down.

Betty was about to run for shelter when she heard a shout. The steps on Spotkins' cart collapsed. Sir Percy had fallen in and was being washed out to sea.

Betty could swim. The waves were high, but

she knew what to do. She picked up the
broken door from their cart and ran across the
sand.

'Hurry!' screamed Lord Jameson. 'He's gone
to the bottom.'

Betty was knocked off her feet by the first
wave, but she pushed the door in front of her
and started to swim.

'You're too late!' screamed Lord Jameson.
'He's dead.'

But Betty's feet had touched something soft.
She left the door and dived down. It was Sir
Percy. She grabbed him by the arms and
pulled him to the top. Then she pushed him
onto the door. He lay there like a jelly-fish,
coughing and spluttering.

Lord Jameson waded out to help. Between
them they got the door back to the beach. Sir
Percy lay there, groaning.

'You'll be all right,' said Betty. 'Try to walk as
far as my Dad's house. He'll give you a warm
drink and some dry clothes.'

Sir Percy said, 'You saved my life, young lady. I shall remember that.'

Late that night, there was a knock on the door. There stood Sir Percy.

He had brought back the clothes he had borrowed. He also gave Betty a golden guinea.

'There's something else,' he said.

'Lord Jameson has decided that the King ought to have his own bathing cart, so he's having one specially made.'

'Oh,' said Charlie. 'Then he won't want ours.'

'No,' said Sir Percy. 'But I want it. We are going to give the King a nice surprise!'

Charlie and Sir Percy went into the front room

and talked. And as they talked they laughed a lot.

On the morning of the King's visit, Charlie Hand's cart disappeared off the beach for a time. When it came back the horse was having a job to pull it.

'What have you got in there?' said Betty.

'Wait and see,' said her father.

Down on the beach a crowd had gathered.

Soon King George arrived with a brand-new bathing cart.

 Everybody cheered as he climbed inside.

The horse dragged the King's bathing cart down to the edge of the sea. It stopped beside Charlie's cart.

The King came out of his cart. He was wearing short linen trousers and no wig. He stood at the top of the back steps and waved.

'Why have we stopped here?' he asked.

At that moment the door of Charlie's cart burst open. Down the steps came seven men with musical instruments.

They waded into the sea and played, 'God Save Great George Our King'.

The crowd sang and cheered. The King was very pleased. 'What a surprise! Who owns that cart?' he said.

Betty curtseyed and Charlie bowed. Lord Jameson said something in the King's ear.

'Good idea!' shouted King George. 'Give that man ten golden guineas. Tomorrow I shall return and we'll have more music!

BATHING IN THE SEA, 1789

Until about 1750, nobody bathed in the sea for fun. Then some doctors said that salt water was good. It helped to cure gout and other illnesses. The sea air made people feel better.

Soon it became the fashion for rich people to take a holiday in seaside boarding houses.

Towns like Scarborough, Brighton and Weymouth grew in size.

People took their clothes off to bathe, so they needed somewhere private to change.

A bathing machine gave them shelter; it took them down to the edge of the sea; sometimes a woman was hired to help people bathe safely.

King George III had his first dip at Weymouth in 1789. A band stood in the sea and played while he bathed. You can still see his bathing machine in the Timewalk Museum at Weymouth.

OTHER HISTORY QUICK READS

QUICK READ NO. 1   (ISBN 1 871173 23 X)

The Juggler and the Jackdaw (1066)
> How a young juggler helped William the
> Conqueror at the Battle of Hastings.

Fight for Your Life (1190)
> Harsh punishments are given for minor
> crimes. Meg is sure her father won't be justly
> treated so she asks King Richard the
> Lionheart for help.

The Ferryman (1215-1216)
> Tom the ferryman sees King John sign the
> Magna Carta which promises justice for all.
> But there is no justice for Tom.

QUICK READ NO. 2 (ISBN 1 871173 24 8)

The Ragged March (1381)
> A story set at the time of the Peasants'
> Revolt.

The Butcher's Book (1477)
> A plot to cheat the printer, Mr Caxton of
> Westminster.

The Deadly Barrels (1642)
> How Guy Fawkes was hired to blow up
> Parliament and why the plot failed.

QUICK READ NO. 4 (ISBN 1 871173 26 4)

Trouble Down the Pit (1842)
   Sam is nothing but trouble when he starts
   work down the coal mine until he redeems
   himself by saving several lives.

Fit for a Queen (1851)
   Ann has to take something very special
   to the Great Exhibition in London but
   someone is trying to stop her.

Bomb Scare! (1942)
   Ruth and her mother find themselves
   trapped in a ruined house with an
   unexploded bomb.

THE QUICK READ TIME-LINE

1000	1066	BOOK ONE
	William the Conqueror	
1100		
1200	1190 The Juggler and the Jackdaw	
	Fight for your Life 1190	
1215 Magna Carta	The Ferryman 1215	
1300		BOOK TWO
1348 First outbreak of the Black Death		
1381 The Peasants' Revolt	The Ragged March 1381	
1400		
1415 Battle of Agincourt		
1450 Wars of the Roses		
1477 William Caxton	The Butcher's Book 1477	
1492 Columbus and the New World		
1500		
1509 King Henry VIII		
1558 Queen Elizabeth I		

1605 Guy Fawkes

1642 Civil War
1666 Great Fire of London

1702 First newspaper
1745 Bonnie Prince Charlie
1760 King George III
1783 American War of Independence

1805 Battle of Trafalgar
1830 First Steam Railway

1851 The Great Exhibition
1854 The Crimean War
1885 First petrol-driven car

1903 Wright Brothers' Aeroplane
1914 First World War
1939 Second World War
1948 First large computer
1969 First man on the moon

1700
1800
1900
2000

Date	Book title	
1605	The Deadly Barrels	
1642	Taking Sides	BOOK THREE
1666	Flames at the Door	
1789	A Royal Splash	
1842	Trouble Down the Pit	BOOK FOUR
1851	Fit for a Queen	
1942	Bomb Scare	